Best of
Lord
GANESHA
Tales

TINY TOT PUBLICATIONS
INDIA

Best of
Lord
GANESHA
Tales

© TINY TOT PUBLICATIONS 2008
This Edition:-2008

Edited by:
Shyam Dua

Published By:
TINY TOT PUBLICATIONS
235, Jagriti Enclave,
Vikas Marg,
Delhi-110092 (INDIA)
Ph.: 2216 7314, 2216 3582,
Fax:- 91-11-22143023
email: tinytotpub@hotmail.com

ISBN : 81-304-0608-X

Illustrated by
Bookmark

CONTENTS

BIRTH OF GANESHA

Lord Shiva lived on the Kailash mountain with Parvati. He had many attendants or *ganas*. The *ganas* obeyed Lord Shiva very sincerely. They enjoyed complete freedom. They were free to go anywhere on the Kailash. Parvati was very annoyed with the *ganas* because they had disturbed even her privacy.

One day while Parvati was taking her bath, Lord Shiva happened to come there. Before going into the bathroom Parvati had directed Nandi not to allow anyone to enter the house. When Nandi saw Lord Shiva, he was confused and thought whether he should let him go inside the house or not. He kept on thinking and Lord Shiva entered the house.

Seeing Lord Shiva, Parvati was embarrassed. She did not like his arrival at that moment. She wanted to get rid of this problem for ever. Therefore, she decided to create a *gana* who would obey only her

orders without fail. Next day, Parvati created an idol of a young boy with the residue left of the herbal paste after massage of her body. Thereafter, she put life and her power into him. Parvati ordered the boy that from then onwards he should obey her orders only, and not listen to anyone else. She also gave him a stick to use as a weapon in time of need. The boy said, "Mother, I will obey your orders."

Parvati said to him, "I am going to take bath. Stand at the door and do not allow anyone to enter the house."

Saying so, Parvati went inside the house.

When she was still taking bath, Lord Shiva came to the house and tried to enter. The boy who was sitting at the gate of the house stopped Shiva and said, "You cannot go inside. My mother is taking bath. She has asked me not to allow anyone to enter the house."

Lord Shiva said, "Don't you know me? I am Shiva, your mother's husband. Let me go inside."

The boy replied, "Whosoever you may be, I won't allow you to enter the house."

Hearing this Shiva said furiously, "How dare you stop me to enter my own house." Saying so, Shiva tried to enter inside but the boy hit him with his stick. Lord Shiva could save himself with great difficulty.

Then he ordered his *ganas*, "Get this boy out of my way. This obstinate boy is stopping me from entering my own house. Go, and push him aside."

As soon as Shiva ordered his *ganas,* they ran towards the boy. The boy beat them all with his stick. They all ran back to Lord Shiva. Seeing the pitiable condition of his *ganas*, Shiva was annoyed. He thought of punishing the boy himself. He threw his *trishul* towards the boy. The boy stopped the *trishul* on its way. Now Shiva realized that the boy was not an ordinary being. So he asked Brahma, Vishnu, Indra and other Gods to help him.

A fierce battle was fought between the boy and other Gods. The boy made all the weapons of the Gods ineffective. They were defeated badly.

Now Shiva thought of a plan to defeat the boy. He made a plan along with Lord Vishnu. Vishnu agreed and challenged the boy for a fight. The boy threw his stick towards Vishnu but his Garuda caught it in his beak. In this way Lord Vishnu was saved.

While both were engaged in fighting, Shiva got an opportunity and attacked the boy from behind. He threw his *trishul* at him. The head of the child was cut off. Shiva killed the creation of Parvati.

After the death of the boy, all Gods and Shiva's ganas were very happy. They praised Lord Shiva.

Meanwhile, hearing the loud noise outside the house, Parvati came out and said "My son! What happened? What is all that noise? Who has come?"

But as soon as she saw the dead body of her son, she stood stunned. She wept bitterly. Thereafter, she shouted furiously and created thousands of *tapasvinies* with her divine power and ordered them, "Go! Destroy the whole universe!"

Looking at the furious mood of Parvati all the Gods went to her and prayed, "Please, be patient and kind to us."

Hearing this Parvati said, "If Lord Shiva makes my son alive again, I would stop all the destruction."

All the Gods rushed to Lord Shiva and conveyed this message of Parvati. Shiva said to his *ganas*, "Bring the head of any creature from the north direction quickly!"

The *ganas* of Lord Shiva proceeded to north immediately. They first saw a tusker in the north

direction. They cut its head at once and brought it to Lord Shiva. Lord Shiva joined the head of the elephant to the body of the child and made him alive again. Thereafter, he blessed the child and named him 'Gajanan'.

Then he said to Gajanan, "You have shown extraordinary courage and bravery, and hence, I appoint you the chief of my *ganas*. You would be worshipped first among the *Gods*. You would also be worshipped first in all the religious ceremonies and would be regarded as the protector from bad omen." Now being the head of the *ganas*, he was called Ganesha. Parvati was informed that her son had been made alive. She was very happy. The news that her son would be worshipped first of all in all the ceremonies made her happier. Since then Ganesha came to be known as the 'first God'.

REALISATION OF MISTAKE

During childhood, Ganesha used to play with the *ganas* of Lord Shiva. He was very naughty and mischievous. He never liked to sit quietly at a place. Inspite of this, he was loved by everyone.

One day while he was playing with *ganas*, he saw a cat. He caught the cat by her tail and began to whirl her. The cat felt great pain and as she tried to get free, she fell on the ground with a thump. She got injuries on her body but managed to run to a safe place.

Now, Ganesha realised his mistake. His intention was not wrong as he just wanted to play with the cat. He repented for the wrong he had done to the cat. Tears began to roll down his eyes.

He came back to his house. He was feeling hungry. He went straight to his mother but was surprised to see his mother with injuries on her body. She was groaning with pain. He could also see some patches of mud on her body.

Seeing his mother in such a pitiable condition was perturbable. He thought that nobody in the universe could even dare to touch his mother. Then how did she get those injuries.

At that moment, he thought about the cat and the rudeness that he had shown to it. Ganesha repented again. He recollected that mother Parvati is omnipresent and has divine powers.

He thought, 'Life is in me as well as in the cat. I hurt the cat and, hence, my mother is hurt. Mother lives in all the creatures, and all the creatures belong to mother Parvati. This is the reality of the universe'.

Realizing his mistake Ganesha wept bitterly. He said sorry to his mother and promised that he would not hurt anyone in future.

Parvati was pleased to see her son's innocence. She hugged him out of love.

THE PIOUS RIVER KAVERI

Once upon a time there was an acute shortage of water in the southern part of India. The people were deprived of even a drop of water. The reason being, there was no river in the region. The people were facing great difficulty due to the shortage of water. To put an end to their plight, the great *muni* Agastya worshipped Lord Brahma. Listening to the muni's prayer Lord Brahma appeared and said, "I am happy with you. Ask for a boon." The *muni* said, "There is an acute shortage of water in south India. There is no river in that region. Kindly solve this problem." Hearing the problem, Lord Brahma poured some pious water into the kamandal of *muni* Agastya and said, "At first, select a proper place in the southern part of India and then sprinkle this pious water there. It would turn into a pious river."

Saying these words Lord Brahma disappeared.

Muni Agastya was very happy to get the boon.

The great *muni* wandered here and there in search of a proper place. Actually, he wanted that the origin of the river should be in such a place from where the need of water of all the people could be fulfilled. He reached Kurg (Kodagu). He liked the place but not so much therefore he continued his search for a better place. Seeing Muni Agastya in a state of confusion, Lord Ganesha wanted to help him. He appeared before him as a child and said. "O Great *muni*! It appears as if you are searching for something. May I help you?" The *muni* replied, "I am in search of a suitable place for the origin of a river. If you really wish to help me, you may accompany me."

Saying these words, Muni Augustya handed over his *kamandal* to the child and proceeded ahead.

The *muni* had hardly covered some distance when the child again said, "O great *muni* ! You seem to be tired. Please take rest. I will continue searching and would return soon.

Muni Agastya stopped to rest under a tree. The child went ahead in search of a place for the origin of river.

After sometime he reached a place which could be suitable for origin of the river. He kept the *kamandal* at that place and rushed back to the *muni*. He was very happy to find the good place and thought that the *muni* would be very glad to know about it. The child who was actually Lord Ganesha in disguise went to the *muni* and explained all the matter to him. He was very happy to know that a proper place was found for the origin of the river. Both of them reached the spot. But they were perturbed to see that a crow was sitting on the *kamandal* which was not a good sign. As the crow flew away some drops fell on the ground from the *kamandal* which took the shape of a giant river. The river came to be known as *Kaveri*. Thus, with the blessings of Lord Ganesha and *Muni* Agastya the river *Kaveri* came into existence in south India.

THE CARRIAGE OF GANESHA

Once all the Gods gathered for a meeting in Lord Indra's court. The king of *Gandharvas* Kraunch also attended the meeting. After the meeting when he was returning in a hurry, he accidently stepped on one foot of the sage Vamdev. The

saint cried with pain and took it as an insult. He thought that Gandharvraj had done it purposely. In a fit of anger, the saint cursed him and said "You will become a mouse."

Hearing the curse, Kraunch fell on the feet of the saint and begged his pardon, "O great sage! Believe me I did it unknowingly. I stepped on your foot accidently. I am very sorry for this. I am really very sorry. Please forgive me!"

Sage Vamdev became sympathetic and said, "Now, I cannot take the curse back. But I bless you that as a mouse you would serve Lord Ganesha as his carriage. You would also be worshipped along with Ganesha. People would treat you as a god. Once Lord Ganesha mounts you all your problems would be solved automatically."

Thereafter, under the curse of Sage Vamdev, Kraunch turned into a mouse and fell on the ground in the *ashram* of sage Parashar. He turned into a very big mouse, bigger than an elephant and had very sharp teeth. The mouse created a nuisance in the *ashram*. He could even cut a hard stone. He harassed all the residents living there.

At that time Lord Ganesha was staying there with saint Parasher and his wife Vatsala. Even saint Parashar was very worried due to the destructive activities of the mouse. One day he said to Ganesha, "Son! We may have to leave the *ashram*."

"Why?" asked Ganesha.

Parasher said, "This big mouse has made our lives a hell. All the residents are disturbed because of him. He causes harm to our cows as well. He cuts everything and troubles the people of the ashram. It is better to shift to some other place."

Ganesha said, "We would not go anywhere out of the fear of a rat. Besides, leaving the *ashram* is not an easy task. I promise you to make this rat a captive and mount him as my carriage."

Saying this Ganesha went out in search of the rat. As soon as he saw the mouse, he threw his divine net on the rat and caught him. The rat tried his best to free himself but failed to do so. His sharp nails

and teeth could not reach Ganesha. The rat tried hard to get rid of the net. Ganesha then took a high jump and sat on the big rat. Now, Ganesha started increasing his weight. The rat felt as though he would die due to suffocation. At this stage he cried at the top of his voice, "Oh lord! I beg your pardon. My powers had made me blind. My life is now in your hands." Ganesha took pity on the rat and reduced his weight. He said to the mouse, "You would be my carriage and I will mount on you." The mouse agreed and said, "I consider myself lucky to be your carriage. I am your servant and will serve you with full dedication."

THE MARRIAGE OF LORD GANESHA

Lord Shiva and Parvati had two sons. The elder was Kartikeya and the younger was Ganesha. Both were brought up with great love and care by Lord Shiva and Parvati. When they reached the marriageable age, Parvati said to Shiva, "*Swami*! both of our sons are grown up now. We should get them married."

Lord Shiva said, "I agree with you but the question is to whom should we get married first. This is the reason I am not able to take any decision."

Parvati said, "That is no dilemma at all. We should go to them and ask them as to who wants to get married first."

They went to their sons and kept the proposal of marriage before them. To their surprise both readily agreed to the proposal. But each of them insisted on getting married first. Kartikeya supported his point by saying that he was elder than Ganesha, while Ganesha said that he was more intelligent than Kartikeya, so he should be married first.

Now, there started an interesting debate between the two sons. Shiva smiled and said, "Both of you are my good sons. Now whosoever completes one round of the earth first would be married first."

Hearing Shiva both the sons stopped arguing. Kartikeya said, " I will go for a round of the earth on my peacock and surely would return earlier than Ganesha whose mouse's speed is nothing in comparison to my peacock's."

Saying these words, Kartikeya touched the feet of his parents and flew away on his peacock.

Ganesha started thinking, 'What should I do? I cannot win the race. My mouse takes such a long time to walk. How will I be able to take one round of the earth? I must think of some trick which would help me to win this competition.'

Ganesha sat in meditation for a while. He thought and thought again. After some time he smiled. He

had thought of an excellent plan in his mind.

Thereafter, Ganesha went for a bath. After taking bath, he prepared two seats for his parents and said to them, "Kindly be seated here."

Shiva and Parvati looked at each other. They failed to understand what the matter was. But they sat as per the desire of their son. Then, Ganesha sat on his mouse and went around his parents seven times. Thereafter, he stood before his parents with folded hands and said, "I have fulfilled your condition. Now, you keep your promise."

Hearing Ganesha, Shiva said, "Which condition and promise are you talking about, my son?"

Ganesha said, "You had said that whosoever between us completes one round of the earth first would get married first. This condition had been put forward by you and Kartikeya and I had accepted it."

Shiva said, "Yes! I had put the condition before both of you. But you have not completed any round of the earth. You did not even move from this place, while Kartikeya left immediately."

Ganesha replied, "I have completed seven rounds around both of you. So, what is the need to go around the earth?"

Hearing it Parvati said, "This is worthless. Taking rounds of your parents does not mean that you have completed a round of the earth."

Ganesha replied, "It is written in our *Vedas* and *Shastras* that if a son takes a round of his parents, it is equivalent to one round of the earth and he would be rewarded by the same virtue. There-fore I have completed seven rounds of the earth." Hearing the intelligent reasoning of Ganesha both, Shiva and Parvati were speechless. They were impressed by

his intelligence. They decided that Ganesha would get married first. Prajapati Vishvaroop's daughters Riddhi Siddhi were selected as Ganesha's brides. The marriage took place in the absence of Kartikeya. When Kartikeya returned from the journey he was very upset to know about Ganesha's marriage. He decided to leave the house. He went to his parents, touched their feet and said, "I have come to seek your blessings. I have decided to leave Kailash and live somewhere else."

"But why my son?" asked Parvati.

Kartikeya replied, "I am disenchanted with this world and want to live alone on the Kraunch mountain. There I would spend my time worshipping the almighty and singing devotional songs in the peaceful atmosphere." Shiva persuaded him to stay back. But Kartikeya was determined to go to Kraunch. At last Shiva allowed him to go.

WHEN MOON WAS CURSED

Once Lord Brahma went to meet Shiva at Kailash. Shiva welcomed him and offered him a seat. While they were discussing some issues, *muni* Narada came there. He greeted both of them. He had brought a fruit for Shiva which he offered to him. Kartikeya and Ganesha also came there and expressed their desire to eat the fruit. Shiva consulted Brahma and said, "Brahmaji! Both my sons are insisting on having the fruit. I am not able to decide to whom I should give the fruit. Please help me in taking this decision."

Brahma said, "Give this fruit to Kartikeya, because he is elder and he has the right to eat it first."

Shiva accepted the advice of Brahma and gave the fruit to Kartikeya. This made Ganesha very angry. Out of anger, he started disturbing the entire world.

He could not control himself and in anger went to Lord Brahma. Seeing Lord Ganesha in great anger,

Brahma trembled with fear. The Moon God was seeing all this and laughed at Ganesha.

Lord Ganesha saw him laughing, which made him more furious. He lost his control and in a fit of anger cursed the Moon, "Oh Moon! From today onward your sight would not be beneficial to anyone. Not only this if anybody sees you, he would be a sinner and would be punished as if he has committed a great sin." Saying this, Lord Ganesha left.

Now, moon was repenting for his action. He had become worthless due to the curse of Lord Ganesha. All the Gods were feeling bad for him. Lord Indra went to Lord Ganesha and said, "Oh! Lord Ganesha, you have always been kind to all and protected everyone. Please forgive Moon."

Ganesha said, "The fourth day of the month of *Bhadrapada-Shukla* would be bad for the people who happened to see the moon."

Thereafter, both the Gods came back and said to Moon, "Lord Ganesha has not freed you from the curse fully. You must please Lord Ganesha to get rid of his curse completely. You should better enchant Ganesha Mantra whole-heartedly and hope for the best."

Saying this they left. Now Moon sat on the bank of the river *Jahanvi* and started worshipping Lord Ganesha.

Ganesha was pleased with Moon's dedication and said, "Now you would regain your lost prestige. People would worship both of us on the fourth day of the month, which is known as *Krishnapaksha*. Your sight would be considered sacred. People will worship your appearance on the second day of every month. This would bring them prosperity."

In this way, moon regained his lost prestige.

TALASUR WAS PARDONED

Once, there was a very powerful devil on the earth.

His name was Talasur. He had acquired destructive powers by his sincere worship and meditation. Now he wanted to conquer Amravati. He was attracted by the extraordinary beauties and enormous wealth of Amravati. When Shukracharya, the *guru* of devils came to know about his ambition, he called him and said, "Talasur, it would be very difficult to conquer Amravati because all the Gods are very powerful. For doing so, you will have to get a boon of immortality from Lord Brahma. Try to please Lord Brahma through meditation."

Talasur started worshipping Lord Brahma. While doing so, he did not take even food and water.

Pleased with his devotion, Lord Brahma appeared before him and told him to ask for a boon. Talasur said with folded hands, "Kindly grant me immortality."

Hearing him, Brahmaji said, "Talasur, granting immortality would be against the rule of nature. You can ask for any other boon."

Talasur was cunning and used the magic of words and said, "I want to conquer the whole world, I wish that no creature, neither Gods nor human beings, could kill me except an elephant."

Brahmaji granted the boon to Talasur and disappeared. On getting the boon, Talasur became very powerful. He thought, 'Now nobody would be able to kill me. So far as elephants are concerned, I will never face one.'

Talasur created a big and strong army of devils and attacked Gods. Gods were not ready for this sudden attack and were defeated badly. Hence, Amravati was conquered by the devils. All the Gods fled. They

were homeless and felt helpless.

The boon granted by Brahma had made Talasur very proud. He thought that now nobody could kill him. He had turned into a tyrant. His atrocities on Gods increased day by day.

At last, all the Gods with their king Indra went to Lord Brahma and they requested him to protect them from cruel Talasur. Hearing the Gods, Brahma said, "I have granted immortality to Talasur. But he can be killed by an elephant. Go to Lord Ganesha whose head is of an elephant. Surely he would help you."

The Gods got some relief on hearing Lord Brahma. They went to Kailash and bowed before Lord Ganesha. They told everything in detail to him, right from the fall of Amravati to the increasing atrocities of devils, and said, "Oh Lord! help us to come out of this problems. Since you have a head of an elephant, you can kill the devil Talasur."

Lord Ganesha assured

the Gods and said, "Don't worry! I would certainly protect you from the tyrant Talasur."

Thereafter, Ganesha took the blessings of his parents and went to Amravati.

On reaching there, he challenged the devil king Talasur. Seeing Lord Ganesha alone, Talasur made fun of him and said, "Come Ganesha, the coward Indra has hidden himself somewhere and has sent you to fight. Now, your death is certain. Nobody can save you."

Actually, the poor devil was quite unaware about Lord Ganesha's power. Lord Ganesha said to him, "Talasur, too much of pride is not good. Pride is the route to downfall."

Talasur ran towards Lord Ganesha with a sword in his hand to kill him. Lord Ganesha wrapped him in his trunk and threw him away. Talasur fell down on the ground and became unconscious.

After some time, when Talasur regained consciousness, he recollected the condition of the boon granted by Lord Brahma. According to the boon, he could be killed by an elephant. He realised that Lord Ganesha could kill him. He immediately fell on the feet of Ganesha and said, "Kindly spare my life. I had become blind out of pride."

Ganesha took pity on him. He forgave him and said, "Leave Amravati at once." Talasur bowed and left at once. The Gods were happy to get Amaravati. They thanked Lord Ganesha.

KILLING OF SINDURASUR

This is the story of *Dwapar Yuga.* One day, Lord Shiva went to meet the creator of the world, Brahmaji along with his wife Parvati. At that time Brahmaji was sleeping. But, on knowing that Lord Shiva and Parvati had come to meet him, he got up. While he was yawning in sleepiness, an attractive youth came out of his mouth. Brahma was surprised to see him and asked, "Who are you, and how did you come here?" That youth said, "I am your son. When you were yawning, I came out of your mouth."

Brahma was happy to see his creation and said, "I am very happy to get a son like you. You will be known as Sindura. I also bestow some boons on you. Nobody will be able to defeat you. You would be very powerful. You can live in any place of your choice."

Sindura was very happy. He bowed and went towards the earth. But on his way he thought, 'I must test the boons granted by my father

Brahma. When I can live anywhere, then why should I live on earth and why not in the heaven?'

With this thought he came back. Seeing his son back Brahma asked, "Why did you c o m e back? Why did you not go to earth?"

Sindura said, "My dear father! I want to testify the reality of your boons on you."

Brahma said in anger, "Oh knave! you want to kill your father! From today you would be known as the devil Sindurasur."

Saying this, Brahma ran for his life. He reached Vishnu and said, "Kindly save my life. My own son wants to kill me."

Vishnu assured him saying, "Don't worry. If he proceed towards you I would cut his head with my *chakra.*"

F o l l o w i n g Brahma, Sindura also reached to catch him. But Vishnu stopped him and said,

"Oh! Sindura, what would you get by killing your old father? If you want to testify the reality of the boons you should go to a young man of your age."

Hearing Vishnu, Sindura said, "That's right! Since you are not old, I would like to have a fight with you."

At this moment, Vishnu thought of a plan and said, "Son! I am the protector of the earth and in case I engage myself in fighting with you, the work of protection will be stopped. Therefore, you should go in search of a person who is equivalent to you."

Sindura thought, 'Vishnu seems to be correct. Surely, I would like to enjoy a fight with a person of my age and strength.'

Thereafter, Sindura proceeded towards Kailash. At that time, Lord Shiva was in meditation and Parvati was waiting for him. Sindura saw Parvati sitting near Shiva and thought of marrying her. He thought, 'This beautiful woman is meant for me. She has nothing to do with this ascetic. It would be useless to fight with this *yogi* at this moment. I will

take away this woman and marry her. There is enough time for doing this.'

Thereafter, Sindura caught hold of the Parvati's hair and began to drag her. Parvati cried for help.

Hearing the cries of Parvati, the *ganas* of Shiva and Nandi tried to help but Sindura defeated them. They ran to Shiva and said, "Oh lord! Kindly protect mother Parvati! A powerful devil is taking her away forcibly. We are unable to stop him."

Hearing all this, Shiva got furious and challenged the devil, "Oh knave! Leave my wife, otherwise I will cut off your head!"

Sindura ignored the threats of Shiva and challenged him for a fight. Lord Shiva and Sindura had a big fight.

Parvati called her son Ganesha for help. Suddenly, a *brahmin* appeared there. He came between Shiva and Sindura and said, "Stop fighting. It is not good. May I know for what the fight is going on?"

Sindura said, "I want to marry this woman. She is wasting her life with this ascetic."

But Shiva said, "Keep your mouth shut. Shame on you! A man can never marry the wife of another man."

Hearing both of them, the *brahmin* said, "I would sit aside with this woman. The one who wins the fight would be entitled to take the woman."

The *brahmin* sat with Parvati, while Shiva and Sindrasur started fighting. It seemed as if their fight would never end. Shiva kept Sindura away with his *Trishul*. Sindura too attacked Shiva now and then.

Now the *brahmin* who was Ganesha in disguise used his divine powers on Sindura. Sindura who had got tired of fighting heard a voice, "Run away from here to save your life. Your opponent is none else but Lord Shiva, the God of Gods, and the woman is Goddess Parvati. You cannot defeat Lord Shiva. Better you run away from here to save your life."

Sindura got frightened and ran away. Hence, Lord Shiva won the fight. Now Ganesha came to his original form. He bowed before his parents and said, "Mother! See, how I chased the devil. I used my powers and frightened Sindura. He would never dare to come here again."

Mother Parvati said, "Had you not come in time, he

would have caused great harm."

"Oh mother! How is it possible that you call your son and your son fails to appear!" said Ganesha.

After this episode, Sindura reached the earth. He conquered whole of the earth and roamed fearlessly. He became so cruel that people ran for their lives here and there to save themselves from him. His atrocities went on increasing day by day.

Sindurasur even attacked Indrapuri, where God Indra stayed and conquered it. The king of Gods, Indra hid himself in the caves of the Sumeru mountain. Later, under the leadership of Indra all the Gods went to *guru* Brihaspati for help and said, "*Gurudev*, Sindurasur has become so powerful that he has made our lives a hell. Please tell how we can protect ourselves from the devil."

Brihaspati said, "I advise you to worship Lord Vinayak (another name of Ganesha). He is very kind and surely would protect you from Sindurasur."

All the Gods started worshipping Lord Vinayak. At last, Vinayak appeared before them and said, "I am pleased with your devotion. You may ask for anything." Gods were surprised to see the attractive personality of Lord Vinayak and said, "Devil Sindurasur has been terrorising us for long. His cruelties have crossed the limit. We cannot bear it anymore."

Hearing the Gods, Lord Vinayak said, "Do not worry now. The days of Sindurasur are numbered. I would be incarnated as the son of Lord Shiva as Gajanan and would kill Sindurasur."

Saying this, Lord Vinayak disappeared.

Now as per the promise made to Gods, Lord Vinayak was born to Parvati. Since the child looked ugly due

to elephant–like head, Parvati refused to accept him as her son and said to Shiva, "How ugly the child is! He has an elephant– like head. Women would make fun of me. Please send him somewhere else."

At first Shiva tried to convince her, "Parvati, this is our son and we should accept him."

But Parvati did not listen. So Shiva had to send him to the queen of Mahishmati whose son had been abducted by a devil during her unconsciousness. But when the queen regained her consciousness, she refused to accept the ugly child and said to the king Varenya, "*Maharaj* ! remove this ugly child from here immediately! I would never accept him under any circumstances."

Seeing the reaction of the queen, the king ordered one of his servants to leave the child in a forest without revealing the child's relation to the royal family. The soldier took the child to the forest and put him near a pond. Fortunately, there was an *ashram* near the pond. A well-known sage Parashar lived there with his wife. The sage saw the child lying near the pond and picked him up with great affection.  He took the child to his house and told his wife Vatsala to nurture the child with great love and care. They called him 'Gajanan'.

Meanwhile, the atrocities of Sindurasur were increasing. Once, while he was sitting in his court, Narada came to meet him and said, "How are you Sindurasur?"

He replied, "All the three realms of the universe and Gods Brahma, Vishnu and Mahesh are afraid of me. No one can defeat me."

But Narada said, "Do not be too proud of your power and strength. For your knowledge, a boy has been born who will defeat you."

"Oh! Why are you joking, Naradaji? I have been

gifted with a boon from Lord Brahma, and hence, am invincible," said Sindurasur.

At this moment, a voice was heard from the sky, "O foolish creature! Your destroyer has already been born at Kailash. The end of your life is very near!"

Hearing this prediction, Sindurasur became very furious and reached Kailash in anger. He frightened Parvati with a sword and said, "Tell me where your son is. I will kill your son who is said to be my destroyer."

Seeing Sindurasur in great anger, Parvati became unconscious. He thought of killing Parvati to finish the matter once and for all.

When Sindurasur was about to kill Parvati, Lord Shiva used his divine power, by virtue of which Parvati turned aside in her unconsciousness and Sindurasur saw her son lying beside Parvati. He immediately picked up the boy and flew away in the sky. While he was on his way, he felt as if the child had become very heavy. Soon Sindura found it hard to carry the child. So, he dropped him below on the earth with the intention of killing him. The child fell and broke into pieces. But Sindura was quite unaware of the divine illusion cast by Lord Shiva and that his destroyer was being fostered at the *ashram* of Sage Parashar. On the other side, many sages assembled at the *ashram* of Parashar. They said, "Now we can not tolerate the atrocities of Sindurasur any more. We do not know who would save us."

Parashar said, "There is always an end of a sinner." He further said, "My son Gajanan would save you from wicked Sindura. He has been incarnated for this purpose."

Gajanan was hearing their discussion. He immediately mounted on his mouse and reached the palace of the Sindura. He almost roared from outside the palace of the devil. The voice was so loud that Sindurasur trembled with fear.

Sindurasur ordered the chief of

his army, "Go outside and find out who wants to be killed by my hands. It seems he does not know he is in my territory and I can kill him any time I want."

The chief of his army went outside to inquire about the matter. He was surprised to see that a giant man with an elephant–like head was sitting on a mouse. He immediately rushed back to Sindurasur and informed him about the danger.

Sindurasur laughed and said, "Being my chief, you are not supposed to be afraid of such a person. I would kill him in no time."

Saying these words, Sindurasur went outside and challenged Gajanan, "O mouse rider! Who are you? Why are you calling your death yourself?"

Gajanan said, "I am son of Lord Shiva. I have come here to kill you." Sindurasur replied, "How dare you say this! Now I'll not spare you."

Both started fighting with their weapons. Sindurasur tried to crush Gajanan but, Gajanan expanded his body to such an extent that Sindurasur could not hug him.

Then, Gajanan picked up Sindurasur by his neck and threw him on the ground. He pressed his neck so hard that his eyes came out and he died instantly. Lord Gajanan rubbed the blood of Sindurasur on his body. Since then the *Sindura* (vermilion) has become a part of his body. With the death of Sindurasur a wave of happiness spread all over. Gajanan was praised by all.

RAVANA AND SHIVALINGA

Ravana, the king of Lanka, was a great devotee of Lord Shiva. He was also a great scholar. He had ten heads. Moreover, he had been granted a boon by Lord Shiva that if any of his heads were cut, it would regenerate again. He used to worship Lord Shiva at the Kailash mountain. He used to cut his head and offer it to Lord Shiva daily. Actually, Ravana wanted to get Shiva's *Linga* which would make him the most powerful man on the earth like Lord Shiva.

Ravana worshipped Lord Shiva with great dedication. He remained without food and water for many days. At last, Shiva was pleased with Ravana. He appeared before him and said, "Ravana, I am happy with you. What do you want?"

Ravana said, "My lord, I want your *linga*, so that I can worship you at my home. Kindly fulfill my wish."

Lord Shiva gave his *linga* (also called *atmalinga*) to Ravana and said, "Never keep it on the ground until

you reach your destination, otherwise it would get fix there and you will not be able to pick it up again." Saying this, Shiva disappeared.

Ravana was very happy to get Shiva's *linga*. He proceeded towards Lanka. On his way to Lanka he wanted to worship Shiva and for that purpose he was in search of a person who would keep *Shivalinga* up in his hands until he had finished his prayer.

On the other side, all the Gods were worried about their safety as after getting Shiva's *linga,* Ravana would become unconquerable. They went to Lord Ganesha and explained the matter. Ganesha assured them and said, "Do not worry. Anyhow, I will take Shiva's *linga* back from Ravana."

All the Gods returned to their places. Thereafter, Ganesha went to the place where Ravana was looking for someone. Ganesha went in disguise as a boy and posed to be a passerby.

The boy purposely passed through the

same passage where Ravana was looking for someone. As soon as Ravana saw the boy, he called him for help. But the boy pretended to be in a hurry. And said, "I am sorry. I am in a hurry."

But Ravana lured him and said, "Come to me. I will give you good things to eat and also will take you for sight-seeing." The boy agreed.

Then Ravana handed over the *Shivalinga* to him and said, "Do not keep it on the ground. I will be back soon after I have offered my prayers to Lord Shiva."

Saying this Ravana went to a nearby river for a bath.

After taking bath Ravana sat and started worshipping Shiva. In the midst, he heard the voice of the boy who was holding the *Shivalinga*. The boy was saying at the top of his voice, "I am unable to keep this *Shivalinga* in my hands anymore because it is too heavy."

Ravana was upset and said, "Please wait a bit. I am just coming."

But the boy, who was actually Ganesha, ignored his request and put the *Shivalinga* on the ground and disappeared.

When Ravana finished his worship, he came back but was shocked to see the *Shivalinga* on the ground.

He tried his best to pick it up but failed. His dream to take the *Shivalinga* to Lanka was shattered. He returned to Lanka empty-handed.

The place where the *Shivalinga* lies is known as *Mahableshwar*. A big temple has been built at this place. Every year thousands of devotees come here for worshipping Lord Shiva.

There is also a temple of Ganesha nearby called *Gokaran* and devotees visit it with the same spirit.

DURASAD TURNED INTO A STATUE

Once upon a time, there was a devil named Durasad

who ruled over the city of Mukund. He was the son of Bhasmasur who once worshipped Lord Shiva and got a boon of being empowered to burn anyone by touching his head with his palm. Later, Durasad also worshipped Shiva in order to get a boon of immortality.

Pleased with his devotion, Shiva appeared before him and said, "Durasad, You would rule for a long period and nobody would be able to defeat you except my son Ganesha." saying this Shiva disappeared.

The boon of Shiva made Durasad mad with power. His atrocities crossed all limits. People all over trembled due to his fear. Gods, sages, human beings all fled for shelter.

Durasad used to attack Gods at his whim and made them run for protection. He felt pleasure in disturbing people during their worship or meditation.

Human beings were cut by him like vegetables. An atmosphere of terror and violence was prevailing all over the universe.

It was well known to Gods that Durasad could not be defeated by them as per the boon granted by Lord Shiva. They approached Lord Brahma and told him the matter. Brahma said, "It is true that you cannot defeat Durasad, but while granting the boon Lord Shiva also made it clear that his son Ganesha would be able to defeat Durasad. Hence, go to Lord Ganesha for help."

The Gods immediately went to Kailash and prayed to Lord Ganesha for help. Ganesha promised to fight against Durasad and assured them that he would

protect them from his atrocities.

Thereafter, Lord Ganesha reached the city Mukund and challenged Durasad. A fierce fight began between the two. Soon, Durasad realised that Lord Ganesha has come for the Gods' help.

Lord Ganesha turned Durasad into a statue and with this his atrocities also came to an end. A wave of happiness spread over the universe.

The statue of Durasad still exists in Varanasi. Durasad prayed to Lord Ganesha to live in Varanasi as Dudhiraj. Lord Ganesha accepted his prayer. Since then the statue has been worshipped by the devotees of Lord Ganesha in Varanasi.

A LESSON WAS TAUGHT TO PARSHURAM

Parshuram was the son of the great sage Jamdagni and Renuka. He made the earth devoid of *Kshatriyas* several times. He was known for his anger and obstinacy.

Once he went to Kailash to get the blessings of Lord Shiva and Parvati. They were taking rest. Both their sons were keeping a watch while their parents were

taking rest. When Parshuram wanted to get in, Ganesha stopped him and said, "Please wait for some time. My parents are taking rest. When they permit, I will take you there."

But Parshuram insisted on going inside and said, "I do not want to disturb them. I want to just offer my *pranam* and seek their blessings."

Ganesha, still firm on his stand refused to allow him to go inside. Now Parshuram became angry and tried to enter by force. But Ganesha blocked the entry. As a result, both were engaged in a verbal fight for quite some time. Neither of them was ready to give up. Soon they indulged into a physical fight

and starting hitting each other.

Kartikeya tried to control both of them, but all in vain. Parshuram pushed Ganesha, who fell on the ground. In retaliation, Ganesha struck him with great force. Now Parshuram raised his hatchet (axe like weapon) to attack Ganesha but he quickly wrapped Parshuram in his trunk and circled him in the air and showed him the whole universe. Thereafter, he threw him on the ground. Again, Lord Ganesha picked him in his trunk and moved him around his head. Parshuram saw Radha-Krishna in heaven and the whole universe. In this way besides punishing Parshuram for his sins, Ganesha provided him a golden opportunity of seeing Gods in heaven.

INCARNATION OF MAHOTKAT

Rudraketu, a *pandit*, lived in one of the cities of Anga Desh. He was a great scholar. His wife Sharda was a pious lady. Both of them worshipped Lord Ganesha.

Sharda gave birth to two sons. They named their sons as Devantak and Narantak. Both the sons were very talented. Gradually, their fame spread all over. Even Gods were anxious to see the boys.

Once sage Narada came to see the sons of Rudraketu. Narada was welcomed by the *pandit*. He requested the sage to see the birth details of the boys and give his opinion. He called his sons and asked them to bow and seek the blessings of the sage.

Narada blessed them and said, "You are very lucky for having such talented boys. They are destined to become kings. They would be extra- ordinarily brave and would conquer all the universe. But......." Narada stopped.

An uneasiness came on the face of the *pandit* who asked, "Is there anything wrong with their lives?"

Narada told him, "Everything would be right, if your sons worship Lord Shiva."

By that time both the sons had come there and they said to Narada, "We would worship Lord Shiva as per your instructions. Please tell us the method of worshipping Him."

Narada told both of them, "Go to the forest and sit in a lonely place. Then chant the sacred words 'Om Namah Shivaya' and keep on praying till Lord Shiva himself appears and grants boon to you." saying this Narada left.

Thereafter, both the brothers went to the forest and sat in meditation for years. They worshipped Lord Shiva with full dedication and perseverance.

After several years of worship, they were able to please Lord Shiva who appeared before them and said, "I am very happy with you. What do you want?"

Both the boys fell on the feet of Shiva and said, "Kindly bless us so that we can rule over the whole universe and be unconquerable."

Shiva granted them this boon and disappeared.

After their wish was granted, both the brothers became proud of their powers. They decided to conquer the entire world. One day, Devantak said to Narantak, "We should not waste time in discussion. You go to the earth and conquer it. I shall proceed towards Amravati."

Accordingly, both the brothers marched towards their decided destinations with their armies. On his way to Amrawati, Devantak was joined by several demon kings. Therefore, he gathered a big army of devils to defeat the Gods at Amrawati. On reaching there,

Devantak challenged Indra, "Leave Amrawati, otherwise you will lose your life."

Indra said, "Go back if you want your well-being!"

Both were adamant to fight. Indra attacked with his *vajra* (long and strong sword type weapon). But it was cut into pieces by Devantak. A fierce battle resulted in the defeat of Gods and they ran to save their lives. Amravati fell in the hands of the demons.

On the other hand, Narantak continued with his campaign to conquer the earth. Nobody could face him. Both the brothers were very proud of their victories.

After winning the two worlds (heaven and earth), Narantak looked towards the world below the earth known as the nether world. It was being ruled by *Nagaraj* (the king of serpents) named Sheshnag. The demons' army attacked and captured the king Sheshnag, who was brought before Narantak. Narantak said to him, "You can save your life if you agree to pay annual taxes to us."

Nagaraj accepted the condition. In this way both the brothers were able to conquer all the three worlds.

Success and power made Devantak and Narantak blind. They started spreading violence all over. They banned the worshipping of the Gods, and the *Vedic* methods of meditation. They prescribed their own methods of worshipping. Gods, sages and people were living under the reign of terror. They killed those who dared to defy their orders. On the other

side, Aditi was very sad. She was the mother of Indra and many others. She said to her husband, the great sage Kashyap, "My sons are facing great hardship. Amrawati has been captured by demons. My sons have no place to live in. Please suggest some way to solve this great problem."

Sage Kashyap said, "I advise you to worship Lord Ganesha. Only Ganesha can kill both Narantak and Devantak."

Aditi sat in a lonely place to worship Lord Ganesha. She chanted the words 'Om Ganeshaya Namah' (humble salutation to Lord Ganesha). She continued to sit in meditation for a long time without food and water. At last, Lord Ganesha was pleased with her worship and devotion. He appeared before her in his full and absolute divine form having ten hands. He was wearing rings in his ears and a garland in his neck. He said to Aditi, "I am very happy with your devotion and prayer. Ask for anything."

Aditi begged with folded hands, "If you are happy with me, kindly take birth from my womb and help my sons to get their kingdom back from the demons. Moreover, please make the universe free from the atrocities of the evil powers."

Lord Ganesha granted the boon and disappeared. After some time, Aditi gave birth to a son, who was an incarnation of Lord Ganesha. She named her son 'Mahotkat'. A wave of happiness spread all over the *ashram*.

The spies of Devantak and Narantak informed them about the birth of Lord Ganesha from Aditi's womb. They also told them that Lord Ganesha had promised her to help the Gods in getting their kingdom back from the devils. Hearing this Devantak said to his brother, "Let us kill the boy before it is too late."

Saying this, he ordered his soldiers to

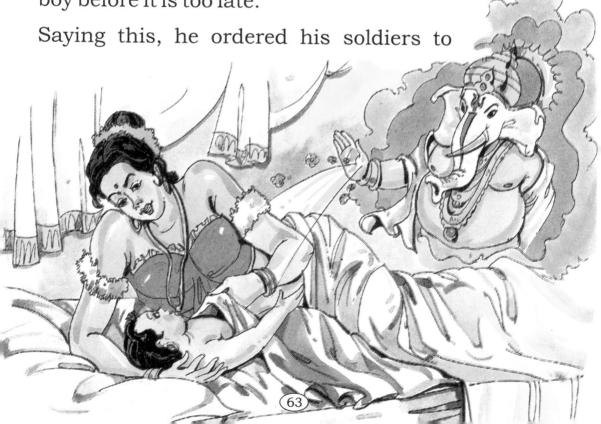

send she-demon Virja. He ordered her to kill Mahotkat. She went to the *ashram*. But the boy Mahotkat recognised her by his divine powers and killed her.

On hearing about the death of Virja, both the brothers were very worried. They realised the seriousness of the situation. Thereafter, they ordered two brave demons Uddhat and Dhundhar to kill Mahotkat. Both the devils reached the *ashram* disguised as parrots.

On reaching there, the parrots flew around Mahotkat and looked for an opportunity to kill the boy. The child was in the lap of his mother. He asked his mother to catch the parrots for him but she said, "My son, they move in the sky. How can I catch them?"

Suddenly, Mahotkat jumped from her lap and caught the parrots by their neck. Both the devils attacked the boy with their beaks and paws and wounded him badly. Mahotkat in turn pressed their neck hard and killed them.

No sooner the parrots, who were demons in disguise, fell on the ground. They changed back into monsters. The ground trembled by their heavy weight. All the people were surprised to see the huge monsters lying dead on the ground. Mother Aditi ran towards her son and picked him quickly. She knew the reality that her son was not an ordinary boy but an incarnation of God Ganesha. All the people praised the bravery of Mahotkat and raised the slogan of 'Jai Ganesha'.

UPNAYAN SANSKAR

The great sage Kashyap invited all the great sages, scholars, well-known *brahmins* and Gods to attend the *Upanayan sanskar* (the ceremony of introducing someone to a guru) of Mahotkat. Ever since the two big demons Uddhat and Dhundhar were killed by Mahotkat, all the Gods were eager to see the brave boy. All had come to attend the function.

The demon Narantak decided to take advantage of this opportunity. He made a plan to kill Mahotkat at this ceremony. He sent for five powerful demons– *Vighat, Pingaksh, Vishal, Pingal* and *Chapal.* He ordered them to go there posing as *brahmins* and kill the boy on getting the first opportunity.

All the five devils dressed as *brahmins* attacked Mahotkat. But before they were able to do any harm, they were recognised. Mohatkat chanted a few *mantras* and threw some grain of rice on them. They were burned alive. A wave of happiness spread

all over the *ashram.*

Thereafter, Lord Brahma blessed him and presented him an ever blooming lotus and said to Kashyap, "Your son is very talented and would conquer the demons. I give gold and cows to him and name him as 'Brihaspati'." Then Lord Shiva came forward and gave him a trident and a *damru* (a musical instrument) and named him 'Virupaksha'.

Lord Vishnu offered him a *kanthahar* (necklace) of diamond and named him as 'Sarvapratham'. Then Parshuram's mother Renuka presented a hatchet and a loin to him and blessed him with the name 'Singh Vahan'. The ocean in the guise of a *brahmin* offered garlands and named him 'Phanirajasan'. The God of fire presented 'fire weapons' and named him 'Dhananjaya'. The God of wind gave his power and named him 'Prabhumpan'. All the Gods gave him something or the other. But Indra, the king of Gods, had some doubts in his mind and saw

nothing extra-ordinary in the boy.

To him, Mahotkat was nothing except the son of sage Kashyap. In this way Mahotkat, was his younger brother.

Mahotkat could make out Indra's inner feelings. He became angry and sparks appeared in his eyes which caused a wild storm. The storm flew, God Indra, away. He was blown to a remote place. He fell down unconscious. On regaining consciousness, Indra saw the whole universe and the gigantic form of the almighty in Mahotkat. Now, Indra realised his mistake and thought, 'Has the almighty been incarnated in the form of Mahotkat? Really, I was wrong!' Thinking so, Indra went to Mahotkat and asked for forgiveness. He said, "Please forgive me, I failed to recognise you. Kindly be pacified." On hearing Indra's request, Lord Mahotkat pardoned King Indra.

VISIT TO KASHI

One day the king of Kashi came to meet the sage Kashyap. The sage welcomed the king and said, "*Maharaj*! What brought you here?"

The king of Kashi said, "O great sage! Actually, my son is going to marry. Since you are my family priest, all the ceremonies would be carried by you. Please come with me to Kashi."

Hearing the king of Kashi, sage Kashyap said, "I am busy in a religious ceremony. Hence, it is not possible for me to go with you. Take my son Mahotkat who would perform all the ceremonies."

But the king hesitated because Mahotkat was just a child. Then, the sage said, "My son knows everything and is a perfect priest."

The king agreed. After taking permission of his parents Mahotkat proceeded towards Kashi with the king. When the chariot of the king was passing through a forest they saw that the younger brother of Rudraketu and the uncle of Narantak, Dhoomraksh worshipping the Sun God. The Sun God appeared before him. Seeing this, the king and Mahotkat got down from the chariot and heard the conversation between them. The Sun God was saying, "I am happy with you. Ask for anything."

The devil said, "Give me a weapon which would make me unconquerable as long as I keep it in my possession."

The Sun God granted his desired boon and disappeared. The very next moment a shining hatchet appeared before the demon from the sky. But before it could reach him, Mahotkat jumped and caught the weapon midway and threw it towards the demon. The demon was cut into two pieces. This

caused a loud sound which shook whole of the forest and many trees also fell down. At that time, two sons of Dhoomraksha, Jahan and Manu, were staying at some distance from the sacred place where their father had been worshipping Sun God. Hearing the ear-splitting sound they rushed to their father. Seeing their father dead, they asked the king of Kashi, "Who killed our father? Tell us! We will kill him immediately." The king of Kashi started trembling with fear and pointed towards Mahotkat. The demons turned to Mahotkat and said, "You look like a child but actually you are a big knave! You killed a person while he was worshipping and in meditation. Shame on you! We will punish you." Jahan interrupted, "Not only the boy but the king of Kashi should also be punished. Cut their heads immediately."

The king of Kashi was frightened and said, "I did nothing wrong. Everything has been done by this boy. He has killed your

father. Punish him and not me." Hearing the thankless talks of the king of Kashi, Mahotkat got furious and said, "You are an ungrateful and timid person. You are supposed to protect me as per your promise made to my parents. But sensing danger to your own life you handed me over to the demons. Shame on you!"

Saying this, he changed into a dreadful form and got many weapons through his divine powers. Both the demons attacked him and tried to kill him. But Mahotkat threw two arrows backed by the power of *mantras* towards the demons which pierced their chest and killed them instantly. Then Mahotkat said to the king of Kashi, "You are not trustworthy. You are coward and selfish. I will not go with you."

The king was now repenting and was sorry. He said, "I could not recognise you. Please forgive me."

He then started singing hymns in praise of Lord Ganesha.

After sometime Mahotkat became polite and said, "Always remember that a person whose safety is your liability must be protected at all costs. Deceiving such a person is the worst sin. If you repeat this again, I would not forgive you." The king of Kashi promised not to repeat it. After getting assurance, Mahotkat proceeded to Kashi with him. On reaching Kashi, a warm welcome was given to both the king and Mahotkat.

On the other hand when Narantak came to know about the death of his uncle and his brothers, he went mad with anger. He thought, 'I am fed up with this boy. I fail to understand how a little boy was able to kill the brave demons. This time I will send the demons having magical powers.'

He immediately called four demons having magical powers. These four demons named Vighant, Dantur, Patang and Vidhul were ordered to kill the boy Mahotkat,

who was now proceeding towards the royal palace with the king.

The four devils reached Kashi. The chariot was yet to reach the palace. In the meantime, two demons Patang and Vidhul spread their magic. They created a heavy storm which engulfed the city of Kashi. The whole city was shadowed by the dark clouds. The king expressed deep worries and said, "What a terrible storm! I have never seen such a storm before. It appears that everything would be ruined. What would happen now?"

Mahotkat said, "Do not worry. It is all being done by Narantak who wants to kill me. Soon they would be killed." Saying this, he raised his right hand and recited a *mantra*. A beam of sharp light appeared there and advanced towards the demons. As the beam reached near the demons, it divided into two parts and entered their bodies. The demons were burnt to death. Thereafter, the storm disappeared and the sky became clear. Now the chariot

proceeded further towards the palace. Then the other two demons Vighant and Dantur appeared and attacked Mahotkat.

But they were recognised and brought to death by Mahotkat. Now the chariot moved further. As they reached the gate of the palace, the chariot was stopped by few ladies who had come for *arti* (ceremonial adoration with kindled lamps). Here the three demons came in the form of two donkeys and one elephant. They proceeded towards Mahotkat. But, they were recognised by him. They were immediately burnt alive by his divine powers. Now, there were no obstacles on their way. All the people of Kashi cheered in praise of Mahotkat who had protected them from the demons.

KILLING OF NARANTAK

Mahotkat had killed the demon Dhoom-raksha and his two sons. This made his wife Shramma very sad. She wanted to take revenge from him.

She went to Narantak. Seeing his aunt, Narantak welcomed her and said, "The death of my uncle and brothers have made me very sad. I am consulting my ministers and planning to kill Mahotkat."

Hearing him, Shramma said, "I myself want to go to take the revenge of the killings of my husband and sons. I have seen how successful you have been in dealing with the enemy. I have lost faith in you."

Narantak consoled his aunt, "Please do not say such words. You should not go there all alone. I would send some demons having supernatural powers."

But Shramma replied, "Your demons have done nothing till now and I don't expect anything from you."

But Narantak again assured her and said, "Believe

me, this time our demons would go with full preparation and kill the boy at any cost."

Shramma was not convinced. She said to Narantak that he should continue with his actions while she would make her own efforts.

Saying this, Shramma proceeded to Kashi immediately. After some time, Narantak also sent some of his powerful demons to Kashi.

Shramma disguised herself as a beautiful, perfumed oil seller and went to Mahotkat. She said, "You are famous for your bravery in the entire universe. You have killed a number of powerful demons. You look tired now. I have a special oil for you which would remove your fatigue."

Mahotkat asked eagerly, "Would your oil really remove my fatigue?"

"Surely it would. Believe me and come here. Let me massage the oil on your body," said Shramma.

Hearing her, Mahotkat went towards the perfumed oil

seller and lay down before her. Shramma massaged the oil on his body. After some time, Mahotkat felt a severe burning sensation. He asked, "Oh! What the hell. What type of oil it was? It is almost burning my body!"

Now Shramma appeared in her original monstrous form. She further said, "It was not oil but a poison for you. You have killed my husband and sons. Now this poisonous oil will kill you."

Hearing her, Mahotkat hit her head hard with a coconut. Her head burst into pieces and she died on the spot. Thereafter, Mahotkat had a bath and felt relaxed. The next day, an astrologer came to the royal court of the king of Kashi. He introduced himself and said, "I am coming from *Gandharva Lok*. My name is Hemjyotirvid. Being an astrologer I can tell you the past, present and the future."

Actually he was a spy of Narantak. The king of Kashi

asked him, "Would you like to tell about Mahotkat?"

The astrologer pretended to read the hand of Mahotkat and said "He has brought misfortune for you and, hence, your kingdom is facing trouble these days."

Hearing the astrologer, the king said, "You are mistaken. Actually, he protected the city from the demons by killing several big demons."

"Yes! He has killed them and now he would kill you and take over your kingdom", said the astrologer.

The king again said, "Is there any way to save Mahotkat from these destructive elements?"

"Yes, there is. But I will have to perform a religious ceremony in a lonely place with Mahotkat" said the astrologer with a crooked smile.

The king of Kashi made arrangements for the

ceremony in the forest and asked Mahotkat to accompany the astrologer.

Mahotkat had already come to know the reality. He was ready to face the demon. When both reached the lonely place, the demon tried to get hold of Mahotkat. But before he could succeed Mahotkat produced a beam of light from his eyes which burnt the demon. Mahotkat returned to the king and told everything that had happened. This made the king worried about his safety. Meanwhile, Narantak got the news of the death of his aunt. He decided to go himself to Kashi. He organised a big army of demons and proceeded towards the city.

On reaching the outskirts of Kashi, his army surrounded the city and started killing the innocent people. When the king came to know about the attack of Narantak, he called for his ministers. At last he attacked the army of demons but was defeated and taken into custody by Narantak. When the queen Ambawati came to know that her husband had been made a captive, she ran to Mahotkat and said, "Oh lord, Kindly protect us from the demon Narantak who has made my husband his prisoner and now he is moving towards the palace."

Mahotkat pacified the queen, "Oh, Ambavati! Do not worry at all. I will free your husband from Narantak but you must keep patience."

On assurance from Lord Mahotkat, the queen went back. Thereafter, Mahotkat used his divine powers and called *Yogmaya* (the Goddess of supernatural

powers). She appeared immediately. Mahotkat ordered her to produce thousands of *yoginies* and eat up the army of Narantak.

The yoginies attacked the demons in a calamitous manner. Mahotkat himself took the form of an extraordinary gigantic creature. Seeing the giant-shaped figure with an extremely wide mouth, Narantak lost his senses and was extremely terrified. He said in a trembling voice, "Who... are you?" Mahotkat said, "I am *Kaal-Purush*, your death. Now nobody can save you."

Narantak ran for his life but *Kaal-Purush* followed him everywhere. Narantak fell on the ground as he was tired of running.

Mahotkat said, "See, I am neither a God, nor a demon, or an animal or a *gandharva* but I will kill you." He caught hold of him by his neck and strangulated him. His army fled. Mahotkat was praised and cheered by all.

DEATH OF DEVANTAK

The news of the death of his brother Narantak, made Devantak loose his temper. He was determined to take the revenge for his death. He collected a big army of demons and proceeded towards Kashi. He destroyed everything on his way. The demons surrounded the city of Kashi.

When the king came to know the situation, he prayed to Mahotkat to save the city. Mahotkat assured the king and said, "Do not worry. Devantak would also be killed like his brother. I advise you to go to the battlefield and soon I would be there."

The king of Kashi along with his army attacked the demons. Thereafter, Mahotkat called Yogmaya (Goddess of supernatural powers) and directed her to attack the army of demons with her eight Goddesses of power.

Yogmaya called all her eight powers, named Anima, Garima, Mahima, Laghima, Prapti, Prakamya, Vashitva, and Ishitva. They reached the battlefield and roared to terrify the enemy. The supernatural powers started killing the demons and chased them away. The commander-in-chief of the demons approached Devantak and said, "The eight powerful Goddesses have chased us out of the battlefield. What should we do now?"

Devantak said, "I must go to the battlefield to encourage our soldiers." Saying this, he went to his soldiers and addressed them, "You are all brave. It will be highly shameful if these women are able to

scare brave people like you. Go ahead and kill them all!"

These words worked like magic. The demon army came back and attacked with full force. But the eight Goddesses chased them again. At this stage Devantak himself came to the battlefield. He covered the area with arrows that shadowed the sun. It became total dark. These arrows released immense heat which made the eight Goddesses unconscious.

Mahotkat was aware of the situation. He immediately called the Riddhi-Siddhi (goddess endowed with supernatural power) and directed her to finish the demons. She challenged the devil king Devantak, "Oh, knave! Come to me. You used fire arms and made my sisters unconscious. But do not think that you are unconquerable. Use all your strength and fight me. Your fire arms would not do any harm to me." Devantak said, "Send the king to fight. I do not wish to fight a woman. Fighting is not meant for the women." Saying this Devantak began to laugh.

The Goddess of intelligence warned him and threw a trident towards him but Devantak escaped it with great agility. Thereafter, he threw all his arrows to kill the Goddess, but not a single arrow could touch her.

Now the Goddess opened her mouth wide and ran towards Devantak to swallow him, saying "O demon! Enter my mouth and satisfy my hunger!"

Seeing the deadly mouth of the Goddess, Devantak ran for his life. His army fled from the battlefield.

Devantak reached his parents and asked for help. They were very upset to see the pathetic condition of their son. They advised him to perform a *yajna* to please Lord Shiva and continue with it till he was pleased with him. They further disclosed that Mahotkat was in fact Ganesha and that only Lord Shiva could help him.

His father further explained, "Lord Ganesha was born with a pledge to finish the demons and give away heaven back to the Gods."

He added, "Once you have pleased Lord Shiva, a white horse would appear from the pious altar of the sacrificial place at the end of the ritual. The special characteristic of the horse is that whosoever rides that horse cannot be defeated by anyone. So far as you fight riding on that white horse, you would be under the protection of Lord Shiva and hence, nobody would be able to defeat you, not even Mahotkat."

Hearing his father, Devantak went to Kailash and

worshipped Shiva for a long time. At last, Lord Shiva was pleased with him. As a result, a white horse appeared from the altar of the place of sacrifice.

Once Devantak was able to get the horse from Shiva, he again collected his army. Thereafter, he proceeded towards Kashi riding on the white horse. On reaching Kashi, Devantak started killing innocent people mercilessly. The king of Kashi went to Mahotkat and said, "Oh lord! Devantak has again come with the horse of Lord Shiva which has made him unconquerable. It would be difficult to win him over this time."

Mahotkat said, "Do not worry at all. I myself would go to the battlefield this time and would kill Devantak."

Saying this, Mahotkat went to the battlefield and challenged Devantak. When Devantak saw him he laughed and said, "You are just a kid and I do not

fight kids. It would be better for you to go home and send someone older." Mahotkat said, "Forget about my age! I have come here to kill you."

Devantak said, "The time only will tell who will kill whom." Saying this he aimed all his arrows on Mahotkat. But not a single arrow was able to touch him. Mahotkat threw a trident towards Devantak but due to Shiva's white horse, it could not kill him. Besides, Mahotkat also used other weapons to kill him but all in vain. Now he thought that, something must be done to have Devantak descended from the horse of Shiva, otherwise he would never be killed. Thinking this, Mahotkat changed into half man and half elephant. Thereafter, he rushed towards Devantak and hit him so hard that he fell from the horse on the ground. Now that Devantak was not on

the divine horse, Mahotkat got the golden opportunity and pushed his long tusk into the belly of Devantak. Devantak died then and there.

As soon as Devantak died, his army fled from the battlefield. At this stage, Mahotkat came back to his original form. A wave of happiness filled the universe. All the Gods showered flowers on Mahotkat.

This is how, Lord Ganesha incarnated as Mahotkat killed the gigantic demons like Devantak and Narantak and saved the entire universe. The Gods regained their lost territory. An atmosphere of peace and prosperity prevailed everywhere.

LORD GANESHA BORN AS VAKRATUND

Once upon a time there was an ambitious demon named Matsar. One day he went to the *guru* of demons, Shukracharya, and said, "Oh, the teacher of demons! Kindly accept my salutation. I want your blessings so that I can fulfill my desire to rule over Indrapuri and enjoy the luxuries of heaven."

Shukrachaya said, "It is good that you are ambitious. But this ambition cannot be fulfilled easily. Indrapuri is ruled by Indra who is very brave and powerful."

Matsar said, "I am also very brave but I do not have the sophisticated weapons like Indra." Shukracharya said, "How can you fight without good weapons. First try to get good weapons. Go and worship Lord Shiva and get his weapons. Meditate him by repeating the sacred words '*Om Namah Shivaya*'."

Matsar bowed before his teacher and went to the forest for meditation. Sitting under the tree he repeated the sacred words *'Om Namah Shivaya'* and continued to worship Shiva for years. At last Shiva appeared before him and said, "I am pleased with you. Ask for a boon."

Matsar said, "Kindly make me unconquerable so that nobody can defeat me."

Lord Shiva granted the boon and disappeared. Matsar now came back to Shukrachrya and said, "Lord Shiva has granted me the boon and now nobody would be able to win against me. I want to conquer all the three worlds. Kindly help me to achieve this goal."

Shukrachrya was very happy to know that Matsar had become unconquerable. He said, "Now you are the king of demons. Organise an

army." Thereafter, Shukracharya made him the king according to the customs and conventions of the demons. Matsar collected a big army and started on his expedition.

First, Matsar conquered the earth. Thereafter,

he proceeded towards the heaven and defeated all the Gods, who ran away to save their lives. Then he attacked the nether world and made it a part of his territory. Thus, Matsar emerged as the great king of whole of the universe. His pride knew no bounds. The army of demons now began to terrorise people everywhere.

Gods, now afraid, approached Lord Vishnu and said, "Oh lord! Help us and save us from the atrocities of Matsar." But Vishnu expressed his inability and told them to go to Lord Brahma.

All the Gods went to Brahma and discussed their problem. Brahma also expressed his inability and told them to go to Lord Shiva.

Now they went to Shiva and put their troubles before him. Hearing the Gods Lord Shiva said, "Do not worry. I would certainly punish him. His death is certain."

Hearing these words, all the Gods and sages were very happy and returned to their places.

On the other hand, when Matsar came to know that Shiva had assured the Gods of punishing him, he became furious. He proceeded towards Kailash with a big army and surrounded the mountain. He challenged Lord Shiva for a fight. A fierce combat took place between the two. Matsar won the fight and conquered Kailash. This victory made him mad with power. He asked his commander- in-chief to look after Kailash and returned.

Now, Gods worshipped Lord Dattatreya who appeared and said, "Go and worship Lord Vakratund, who is a mighty and furious form of Lord Ganesha. Please him and he would certainly kill the demon Matsar. The sacred word for him is 'Gang'."

Gods worshipped Vakratund who appeared and said, "I am happy with you. Ask for anything."

The Gods asked for his help. Vakratund said, "Do not worry. I would kill him soon."

Thereafter, Lord Vakratund produced his *ganas* from the fire of *yajna*. Numerous deadly form of *ganas* appeared. Lord Vakratund ordered them, "Go and seize the capital of Matsar. Kill all the demons. I shall fight Matsar."

All the *ganas* left immediately and proceeded towards the capital of Matsar and surrounded it. When the demon came to know, he sent his two sons, Sunderpriya and Sarvapriya, to kill Vakratund.

Both the sons of Matsar went to the battlefield and challanged Lord Vakratund. A fierce battle started. The Gods were fighting from the side of the

ganas. Shiva also fought with them and killed the demons with his trident. The sons of Matsar tried to catch Shiva using a net but the ganas killed them. The commander-in-chief of the demons took the possession of the dead bodies of the sons of Matsar and ran towards the capital. The army of the demons also fled from the battlefield. At that time, Indra suggested Lord Varkatund to chase the demons and defeat them completely.

But Vakratund said, "No, we must not do this as Matsar would be in sorrow because of the death of both his sons. He would come to fight to take his revenge. That would be the time to kill him."

When Matsar saw the dead bodies of his sons he lost his cool and asked his army to march to the battlefield. He himself led the army.

A big fight took place between Lord Vakratund and Matsar. At last the demons were defeated and Matsar surrendered himself. He begged for forgiveness and said, "I was wrong and mistook you as an ordinary God. Kindly have pity on me." Lord Vakratund took pity on Matsar and forgave him. He said to him, "I am happy that you are repenting for your misdeeds. But I warn you not to repeat it. In case you repeat your actions, I would come again and kill you."

Matsar promised Lord Ganesha that he would lead a pious life. Hence, the atrocities of the demons stopped and the Gods regained their heaven. Sages and all the other people on the earth lived in peace again.

INCARNATION OF MAYURESHWAR

This is the saga of *Tretayug* (the second period of world's existence). There was a famous city named Gandki in the country of Maithil. The king of Maithil was very brave, pious and well-mannered. His name was Chakrapani. His wife Ugra was also a religious lady. They had everything, but were childless. This was a matter of worry because they had no successor.

One day a great sage, Shaunak, visited the palace of the king. The king and the queen welcomed the sage and showed great hospitality. The sage was very pleased and said, "I am very happy with your hospitality. Tell me if I can do anything for you."

The king said, "Oh, great sage! God has given us every-thing. But we have no child. We are always worried about the future of the kingdom. Who would look after it?"

The sage advised them, "You

should worship Sun-God. His worship should be started with the meditation of Lord Ganesha, who is worshipped first among all the deities. If you please the Sun God, he would bless you with a son."

Next day, the king Charkrapani started worshipping Sun-God. The God was pleased with the King and blessed him. The blessings of the God came true and a son was born to the queen. But the boy had three eyes and a fearful face. The queen got frightened and threw the boy in the sea. Thereafter, she told everything to the king. The king was annoyed to hear this. He said, "Ugra! You have committed a sin. We had a son after years of prayers and that too you have thrown into the sea."

The sea took the form of a brahmin and brought the boy to the king. The king was very happy and thanked the sea a lot. The queen also accepted her son and named him Sindhu. The capital city was

decorated as if Diwali was being celebrated. A wave of happiness swept through the city.

Gradually, Sindhu grew into an extraordinarily brave youth. He could uproot a tree easily and could break the head of an elephant. One day Sindhu said to his father, "I want to do something great in life. I feel as though I am wasting my life here."

The king asked, "What do you want to do?"

Sindhu said, "I want to worship such a God who could bless me with the boon of invincibility. By virtue of this boon, I would conquer all the three worlds and fulfill my desire to rule over the whole universe."

His father became very happy to know the high ambition of his son. He said, "My son, it is good that you want to meditate. I advise you to worship the Sun-God because you were born by his blessings."

Sindhu Said, "All right, I would worship Sun God."

Thereafter, he went in a forest and started worshipping Sun. He stood on one leg for several years. At last, the Sun God was pleased with him and told him to ask for a boon.

Sindhu bowed before the Sun and said, "Oh God make me immortal. I want to conquer all the Gods."

Giving him a pot Sun- God said, "Always keep this pot with you and nobody would be able to kill you. If you loose it somehow your death would be sure."

After receiving the boon, Sindhu came back to his parents. They were very happy to know that their son had become unconquerable. The king said, "We are old now and want to spend our time in the service of the

almighty. Now you are the king of this kingdom."

Sindhu bowed before the wishes of his parents and became the king of Maithil.

Sindhu wanted to expand his army and admitted all type of demons and wicked spirits in it. Then, he brought whole of the earth under his control.

Thereafter, Sindhu attacked Amravati where Gods lived. A fierce fight took place between Gods and demons. Sindhu first hit Indra's white elephant Airavat and then attacked Indra with his *Vajra* (a kind of weapon) which made him unconscious. The wounded elephant Airavat ran away from the battlefield taking his unconscious master Indra with him. Amarvati fell in the hands of the demons.

All the Gods went to Lord Vishnu and said, "The demon Sindhu has taken over Amravati and we are running for our lives. Kindly help us."

Lord Vishnu said, "Do not worry. I would teach him a lesson and would get Amravati back."

Saying this, Vishnu went to Amravati and challenged Sindhu. There was a big fight between Vishnu and Sindhu. Vishnu took out his *chakra* (circular weapon) to throw it on Sindhu. But Sindhu quickly hit on Vishnu's hand which made the *chakra* fall on the ground. In a fit of anger, Vishnu hit him with his mace but Sindhu jumped aside and snatched the mace. Now Vishnu had no weapon. Sindhu caught him by the neck and made him a captive.

Vishnu said, "You are very brave. I am happy with

you. You may ask for a boon if you wish to."

Hearing Vishnu, the demon laughed and said, "What can I expect from a defeated God. I have everything. But if you insist, come with me to my capital Gandki and accept my hospitality."

Vishnu gave his consent. Sindhu directed his commander-in-chief to take the possession of *Vishnulok*. He then came back to his capital Gandki along with Vishnu. After making Vishnu his captive, Sindhu became mad with power and increased his atrocities.

All the Gods went to Guru Brihaspati and asked for help. But he expressed his inability and advised them, "Why don't you go to Lord Brahma. He would certainly help you by suggesting some way."

Thereafter, all the Gods along with Guru Brihaspati went to Lord Brahma. He said, "I am unable to help you but if you worship Lord Ganesha he would certainly help you in this regard."

According to the instructions of Lord

Brahma, all the Gods started worshipping Lord Ganesha on the bank of the river Gandki. They carried out a *yajna*. At the end of the *yajna* a beam of light appeared and Lord Ganesha came out of it.

He said, "O Gods! I am happy with all of you. Ask for a boon."

All the Gods said with folded hands, "You are omniscient. The atrocities of Sindhu are increasing day by day. We are living under his constant fear. Kindly save our lives."

Lord Ganesha said, "Time has come to kill the wicked Sindhu. I would be born to Mata Parvati as Mayureshwar and would kill Sindhu." Saying these words Ganesha disappeared. As promised to Gods, Lord Ganesha was born to Parvati as Mayureshwar and killed Sindhu. In this way Ganesha helped the Gods in getting Amravati back.

GANESHA PROTECTED HIS MOTHER

Mata Parvati was not happy with the *ganas* (divine attendants) of Shiva. They enjoyed full freedom and often disturbed mother Parvati's privacy. They would enter her palace at any time. Sometimes they would even disobey her.

At last, Parvati requested Lord Vishwakarma who was the builder of her palace to guard her palace. She said, "I am fed up with the capriciousness of Shiva's *ganas*. They are more faithful to Shiva than me. They even disturb my privacy." Hearing her, Vishwakarma agreed to guard the palace.

During that period, there was a powerful demon named Tarkasur. It had been predicted that he would be killed by the son of Shiva-Parvati. Therefore, the demon wanted to kill Shiva to save his own life. But he was defeated by Lord Shiva. This made him furious and now he wanted to take revenge. He sent his son Shangharak to conquer *Shivlok* (Shiva's territory).

As directed by his father, Shangharak proceeded

towards Kailash and attacked the followers of Shiva. They were tortured by the demons. All the *ganas* and Vishvakarma too faught bravely, but were defeated. Vishwakarma

was made a prisoner. Shangharak went to Shiva's palace. At that time, Parvati asked Ganesha to guard the palace. Ganesha stood outside the palace to guard it.

The demon cried at the top of his voice, "Is there anyone who would accept my challenge and come forward to fight me?"

Thereafter, he ordered his soldiers to enter the palace to confine Parvati and bring her outside.

When Ganesha heard the demon, he got furious and came forward. He said in anger, "Oh demon! Stop! Nobody would be allowed to enter the palace." Shangharak said, "Who are you? How dare you talk to me in this way!"

"I am Ganesha. My mother has asked me to guard the palace. I won't allow anyone to enter the palace without her permission," said Ganesha.

"Do you know who I am"? he asked and answered, "I am son of Tarkasur. I have conquered the whole of Kailash and now I would take the possession of the palace and capture Parvati."

Ganesha was even more infuriated. He roared, "You would never succeed in your mission. You knave! Run from here if you wish to save you life!"

Shangharak laughed and said, "O, child! Your days are meant to be spent in playing. You are unaware of my powers. Hence, I advise you to move away from here." Ganesha said, "You have committed a great sin, I must punish you."

Shangharak said, "Oh! You want to punish me. Get away from here otherwise I will kill you."

"Oh fool! You are taking me too lightly. Let us fight." Saying this Ganesha rushed to the demon and a fierce fight started between them. The combat

seemed to be never ending. At last Ganesha hit him hard by his *gadda*. The demon fell on the ground unconscious. Ganesha freed Vishvakarma from the prison. Vishvakarma said to Ganesha, "The demon had challenged me. Now cut both his hands so that he does not dare to attack Kailash again."

Vishvakarma cut the hands of Shangharak. Seeing this dreadful sight, the army of demons fled from the battlefield. Vishvakarma was very pleased with Ganesha's bravery and said, "Oh brave child! Who are you? You have saved *Shivlok* today."

Ganesha humbly said, "I am the son of Parvati. I am guarding the palace by her orders. Without her permission nobody can enter the palace. I have protected my mother. It was my duty." Vishvakarma was happy to hear these words. This is how Lord Ganesha protected his mother and saved *Shivlok*.

THE IMPORTANCE OF LORD GANESHA

Lord Vishnu, the protector of the world, was going to marry the Goddess of wealth Laxmi. He invited all the Gods to attend his marriage. It was already decided that the marriage ceremony would take place at the residence of Goddess Laxmi at Kundanpur. Lord Vishnu asked all his friends to come to his residence at Baikunthdham. The marriage procession would proceed to Kundanpur from Baikunthdham.

On the day of marriage, all the Gods dressed themselves in their best attire. They wanted to impress the Goddess Laxmi and other people by their luxuries and wealth. They were all looking very attractive.

Now, when they were about to leave for Kundanpur, Ganesha also came there. He had also been invited. Seeing Ganesha, the other Gods became upset. They did not want to take Ganesha along with them. They quickly arranged a meeting and decided that if

Ganesha joined the marriage procession, nobody would go to Kundanpur. The decision was conveyed to Lord Vishnu. Hearing the Gods Vishnu was upset. He said to them, "You are talking in a very strange way. What harm Ganesha is doing to you." All the Gods spoke at once, "Ganesha's presence is a problem. At first, he eats too much. Secondly, his head is just like an elephant. Thirdly, his belly is like a balloon and his feet are large and ugly. We are all handsome and attractive. We shall feel insulted if we go with Ganesha. All the girls of Kundanpur would make fun of us. As such we have decided not to take Ganesha with us."

Hearing the Gods, Vishnu was in a dilemma about how to tackle the problem. He wanted Ganesha to attend the marriage ceremony, but the Gods had already taken the decision to leave Ganesha behind.

Now Lord Vishnu had to take a decision. He had to select between the Gods and Ganesha.

Lord Vishnu was confused. He thought again and

again to find out a solution. Vishnu tried to convince them, "Listen to me seriously, I myself have invited Ganesha to attend the marriage. How can I ask him to go from here? He is my guest at this moment. I cannot stop him from joining the marriage party." The Gods replied, "Lord Ganesha is very innocent. Make an excuse. You may ask him to stay back in heaven for its protection, saying that demons may attack the heaven in absence of other Gods. He is brave enough and can fight all the demon alone. We believe if you use such words, he would be pleased."

At last, Vishnu bowed before the obstinacy of Gods and made the same excuse before Lord Ganesha.

Ganesha was very sad to miss marriage ceremony. He stayed back as desired by Vishnu.

The marriage party proceeded leaving Ganesha back in heaven.

The sage Narada had heard the conversation of Gods

and Vishnu. He went to Ganesha and told everything to him. Ganesha was sad to know the motive of Gods. He said to Narada, "I am very sad to know the opinion of Gods about me."

Narada said, "We should teach a lesson to Gods." "But how?" asked Ganesha.

Narada smiled and said, "Very simple! Ask your *Mooshakraj* (king of rats and the mount of Ganesha) to dig the route the marriage procession would take to reach Kundanpur. When the chariot of Vishnu would pass through the route, it would get stuck in the pits and, hence, they would not be able to proceed any further without your help."

Lord Ganesha was very pleased to hear Narada. As

suggested by Narada he ordered *Mooshakraj* to dig the route.

Now, when Lord Vishnu's chariot reached there, it got stuck in the pit and the marriage party could not go ahead. All the Gods tried their best to pull the chariot forward but could not succeed.

At this moment, a farmer appeared there. He saw that the Gods were making all their efforts to move the wheel but to no use. He went to the Gods and offered to help them saying, "Give me an opportunity if you don't mind. I can lift the wheel up."

Gods were surprised to hear the farmer. Though they were not sure that he would succeed, they allowed the farmer to try.

The farmer uttered the words *'Jai Ganesha'*, applied his full strength and lifted the wheel up. The Gods were astonished. They thanked the farmer. One of the Gods asked the farmer "Why did you utter the word 'Ganesha' while picking up the wheel?"

The farmer was surprised at their ignorance and said, "Lord Ganesha is an obstacle-remover. On all the auspicious occasions we worship Ganesha first. I worship Ganesha before starting any work to achieve success, and the magic of remembering his name before any work has been just proved by me."

Hearing him, all Gods bowed their heads and repented for their folly. The words of the farmer made them realize that outward appearance is not important and a good person is recognised by his deeds.

PRIDE OF KUBER SHATTERED

Pride leads to downfall. Almost all the Gods, sages and human beings have been the victims of pride. Once Kuber, the God of wealth, was too proud of his wealth and luxuries. Once he invited Lord Shiva and Parvati to his house for a meal. But Shiva and Parvati showed their inability and said, "Due to some work elsewhere we are unable to accept your hospitality. But you may take our son Ganesha to your home."

Hearing them, Kuber said, "It would be better if you came for a meal, but since you are unable to do so, let the child come to my house." Then he said proudly, "I can feed thousands of children like Ganesha. Do not worry. I would make good arrangements for Ganesha"

Saying this, Kuber came back home. He asked his servants to prepare good food for Ganesha. Accordingly, they made variety of delicious food.

Ganesha came at the right time to his house. Kuber welcomed him and showed him the palace. After some time, Ganesha felt hungry. Kuber took him to the dining room and asked him to eat as much as he desired. All his servants got busy in serving food to Ganesha. Within no time he finished all the food served to him and asked for more and more. Then the food served to him again was eaten up quickly by Ganesha. This way Ganesha ate up all the food. Now Kuber made arrangements for food from the nearby places. But

that too proved to be insufficient. Ganesha's hunger was not satisfied.

When nothing was left in the name of food, Ganesha started eating other things. Seeing this Kuber felt insulted. Ganesha said to Kuber, "You are a big liar. You promised my parents to feed me well. But there is no food at all. Now I will eat you to satisfy my hunger. Save your life if you can!"

Hearing Ganesha, Kuber ran for his life. He went to Kailash and prayed to Shiva, "Oh Lord! Save my life. I am unable to satisfy Ganesha's hunger. All the food is finished. Now he wants to eat me up to satisfy his hunger. I had thought that being a child Ganesha could be fed easily. But Ganesha seems to have a voracious appetite. I was proud of my wealth and prosperity but a mere child was enough to shatter my false pride. Now my life is at a rick. Please protect me!" Hearing Kuber Shiva said, "Kuber! You

are the God of wealth, but it does not mean that you should be proud of your wealth. I am happy that you have realised your mistake. Remember! pride always leads a person towards his downfall. Surrender your pride. Give Ganesha a fist-full of rice and his hunger would be satisfied."

After hearing Lord Shiva, Kuber came back. He saw Ganesha who was still hungry. He was eating some thing or the other. His hunger was not yet satisfied. Now Kuber offered rice in a bowl to Ganesha with great respect and said to him, "Kindly accept this rice. I had become blind because of my pride. I also underestimated you. Now I have realised my mistake and known your greatness. Please forgive me!"

Lord Ganesha accepted the rice happily and forgave Kuber. As soon as he ate the rice, his appetite was satisfied. He blessed Kuber and left.

MAHABHARATA AND GANESHA

The battle of *Mahabharata* was fought thousands of years back. The battle was fought between the *Pandavas* and the *Kauravas*. The great epic of *Mahabharata* was written by the great sage Vedvyasa. He wanted the people to know about the battle fought between the *Kauravas* and the *Pandavas*. Sage Vedvaysa was very wise and learned.

When Vedvyasa decided to compose *Mahabharata*, he wished to hand over the responsibility of writing it down to Lord Ganesha. Vedvaysa knew it well that the process of thinking and writing cannot go simultaneously and, hence, he requested Lord Ganesha to write down the epic.

Sage Vedvyasa went to Ganesha and requested him, "Oh! Vinayak! You are a great scholar and a learned God. Please help me in writing the epic *Mahabharata*.

I will collect the stories and you write them down. Only you are capable of writing it efficiently. Hence, I request you to help me with it."

Ganesha was busy. He had other work. Moreover, he was not interested in writing the epic and did not want to be an assistant of the sage. But as he had great regard for the sage, he accepted the proposal.

Ganesha kept a condition before the sage, "You'll have to speak continuously. If you stop speaking, I will stop writing immediately and the epic would never be completed. In case you accept my condition, then I would surely assist in your work, otherwise I would not be able to do it."

The sage interrupted, "Yes! I agree to your condition." Sage Vyasa further spoke, "Oh lord! My only request is that whatever I speak must be first understood well and then written." Ganesha said, "All right, I would understand the subject matter before writing." Ganesha accompanied Vedvyasa

and both occupied their seats.

Mahabharata was written in poetic stanzas with rhythm. Vedvyasa spoke in a lyrical manner and Ganesha quickly understood the stanzas before writing them. This process went on for three years. Sometimes, Vedvyasa spoke very quickly and sometimes slowly, but Ganesha was able to maintain his speed of writing. At times, when Vedvyasa was tired of speaking, he spoke very difficult stanzas which compelled Lord Ganesha to think a little and stop writing for some time. This gave enough time to Vedvyasa to take rest.

This way both the great scholars did a lot of hard work to complete the great epic. It is said that there are one lakh stanzas in the great epic of *Mahabharata*. It is also believed that few stanzas are missing. Ganesha's contribution in helping Vedvyasa write the great epic is worth praising.

GANESHA AND LAXMI

Once Goddess Parvati decided to celebrate the *Pattabhishek ceremony* of her son Ganesha. She wanted to celebrate this ceremony with great pomp and show. She invited all the Gods, Goddesses and sages.

Mother Parvati wanted her son to wear colourful dress and so she had selected beautiful, shining and colourful clothes for him. On the day of the function, all the guests came bedecked in their best dresses. But, Ganesha wore white clothes instead of coloured costume. Seeing her son in a white dress, mother Parvati said, "You are supposed to wear a coloured dress but you have worn a white one. Hence, you would be called 'Shuklamberdhar". Ganesha, explaining the significance of white colour said, "White colour stands for purity, peace, cleanliness, good nature and knowledge. Hence I have worn it." Mother Parvati did not argue with her son and kept silent. She was happy to see that the ceremony was being celebrated with great pomp and show.

After the ceremony Lord Vishnu along with Goddess Laxmi blessed Ganesha. But Laxmi was in a hurry and quickly turned to leave. At this moment Vishnu said to her, "Listen, where are you going? We came together and would go together. Please wait for sometime." But Laxmi found it hard to stay and was about to leave.

Vishnu said to Ganesha, "Oh Lord Ganesha! Laxmi has a capricious nature. She can not stay for long at one place." Hearing Vishnu, Ganesha smiled. Vishnu continued to say, "Oh lord! Kindly make Laxmi sit in your lap. Perhaps it would make Laxmi more stable." Hearing this, Ganesha said, "I would be lucky to have Mother Laxmi in my lap. I would be the happiest person in the whole universe." Saying this Ganesha picked up Laxmi by his trunk and put her in his lap.

Goddess Laxmi could not understand what was going on. Vishnu said, "Now Ganesha has become- *Laxmi-ganpati*. It means getting the blessings of Ganesha would mean getting the blessings of Laxmi." The atmosphere was filled with joy when the Gods cheered out the name *Laxmi-ganpati*. Since then, Ganesha is often shown accompanied by Laxmi.

LORD GANESHA AND BHAIRAV

Once Lord Ganesha went wandering on his carriage. While he was roaming in the sky across the Vindhyachal mountains towards the south, he saw some people singing and dancing on the earth. Out of curiosity, Ganesha landed on a big black mountain. The area was covered by banana trees. The people there belonged to the Shabar caste and resided in the sub-mountainous region of Vindhyachal. They were beating drums and dancing to a tune of music.

Ganesha understood that the people were celebrating some function. He disguised himself as a child and went to them. Seeing a child the people jumped with joy and said, "Our God has sent this boy. He is so kind to us!"

They picked up the boy who was actually Ganesha and took him to the altar of sacrifice. There was already a deaf and dumb boy standing there. He was crying bitterly. The whole of his body was smeared with turmeric power. He was wearing black clothes and was extremely frightened.

Seeing the child, Ganesha said to their leader, "I want to talk to your God. Please take me to Him."

But the leader laughed and said, "Our God is darker than darkness. He is so horrible that if you see him, you would die out of fright. Hence, it is better not to go to our God."

Ignoring the leader's words, Ganesha went to the black rock that symbolised their God, quickly and said, "You are afraid of your own fear. You think your God is horrible. But your fear is baseless."

Lord Ganesha continued to say, "Has anyone seen your God? Has your God ever asked for sacrifice? Actually your God is not such as you think him to be. It is your fear that has shadowed your thinking. Think in a positive manner and not in negative one.

Your God is actually very good looking and attractive."

Saying this, Ganesha patted the rock with his palm. To the surprise of all, the rock changed to a beautiful statue. It was in a sitting posture keeping its hands on the knees. All were awestruck when they saw this.

Thereafter, Lord Ganesha blessed the dumb and deaf child by putting his hand on his head. The child immediately cried, "*Swamiji!* give me shelter." Then the boy started singing prayers.

These charismas made the people more fearful than before. They bowed before Ganesha thinking him to be a supernatural power.

Ganesha advised them not to be sacred of him. He further said, "Treat your God as your father, brother or friend. Stop the custom of sacrificing and replace it by offering flowers, fruits and bananas. Celebrate the festival with devotion and reverence. This dumb child who has got the power of speaking would act as your priest and *guru*. Now, I am going to make your God appear before you." Saying this Ganesha climbed up the mountain. Some of the Shabars also followed him to some distance but returned. On reaching the top of the mountain, Ganesha saw Bhairav Swami who was sitting with his head down. His body was black and he looked sad. Ganesha rushed to him and hugged him hard. Now another miracle occurred, the black colour of Bhirav changed to shining white colour. Bhairav said, "I know you are the obstacle remover, Lord Ganesha. When I was incarnated, there was a voice from the sky that by your blessings, my colour would change to white. Nobody dared to climb this mountain. Even the birds kept away out of fear. I had been waiting for you with my horrible colour and ugly shape for years. Now that my problems are solved, I request you to show me your real form."

Hearing Bhairav, Ganesha came to his real form and said to

Bhairav, "From today onwards you would be worshipped as God since you have both Shiva and Keshava within you. Ever since my mother has told about you, I was keen to see you. You have been incarnated with the powers of both Vishnu and Shiva. There is none equivalent to you. Shabar people have been worshipping you for long. Hence, appear before them and bless them."

Bhairav said, "As you wish." Thereafter, Ganesha returned to Shabars as a child and said, "All of you should bow before the statue of you God and say loudly–'we have come to your shelter. We request you to appear before us and bless us'." Ganesha

continued to say further, "Whenever you call your God with true heart, he would appear before you. Live like human beings and your God would always shower your blessings on you." Saying this Ganesha disappeared. Shabars were very surprised. As instructed by Ganesha they called their God and bowed before his statue. Soon their God appeared and blessed them. Thereafter, he disappeared.

The Shabars were very happy to see their God who was very attractive contrary to their earlier belief, that their God was as black as coal and very ugly.

The mystery of the child remained unsolved. They thought that it was their own God who had come in the form of a child and blessed the dumb and deaf child with the power of speech and hearing.

They were very happy that their God himself had come to bless them.

PROTECTION OF YAJNA

Once upon a time there was a king named Sagar. Once one of his successors Abhinand decided to perform a *yajna*. He invited all the Gods except the king of Gods, Indra. When Indra came to know about it, he felt insulted. He wanted to take revenge.

So, he went to the God of death, Yamraj and said, "Abhinand, one of the successors of Sagar has not invited me to the *yajna* ceremony and hence, I am feeling very insulted and want to take revenge. He has knowingly ignored me and he must be punished for that . I request you to kill him."

Yamraj is the only God who is believed to control the

time and decide the life span of a person. That is why he is also known as *kalyam*, which means 'the controller of time'.

The God of death accepted the request of Indra. He went straight to the place of *yajna* and appeared as a giant demon from the fire of the *yajna*. Seeing a

dreadful gigantic figure coming out of the *yajna* fire, all the Gods and sages ran away for their life. There was a stampede at the venue of *yajna* and, hence, the process of worshipping stopped.

Meanwhile *guru* Vashistha asked the king Abhinand to make a statue of Ganesha and worship it. He said, "Ganesha is the God who removes all obstacles from the path of success. Place a statue of Lord Ganesha at the place of *yajna*. Thereafter, worship Lord Ganesha. The ceremony would be completed without any interruption. Also use turmeric while worshiping Ganesha."

King Abhinand started worshipping Ganesha and enchanted the holy words *'Om Ganeshaya Namah'*. The moment he uttered these words thousands of rats appeared and started biting the gigantic figure. The giant figure could not tolerate the sudden attack of numerous rats and quickly disappeared.

After sometime, Yamraj appeared again and threw his strong and heavy noose on the king Abhinand to take his life out. Though the king tried to cut the noose, but failed to reduce its strength and as a result could not free himself.

At this stage his *guru* Vashistha said, "You would not be able to make yourself free from the noose of *Kalyam*. Now only Lord Ganesha can save you. Worship him and he would save you."

The king started worshipping Ganesha in his heart. The very next moment Lord Ganesha appeared with a strong noose which he threw on Kalyam to catch hold of him. But Kalyam quickly changed to Vighnasur (demon of obstacles).

Now a fight started between Vighnasur (Kalyam) and Vighneshwer (Ganesha). The fight continued for a long time.

At last, Ganesha attacked Kalyam with great force and made him unconscious. When he regained consciousness, he said to Lord Ganesha with folded hands "Oh Lord! I can never defeat you. I was foolish

to fight with you. You control the universe. Even the sun rises and sets as per your wishes. I beg your pardon. I have not done it by myself, I was just following the order of the king Indra."

Ganesha forgave Kalyam and said, "Why do you follow others? All your work is pre-decided and you have to work according to it. You should not follow others. Rather, you must take independent decisions.

"You are right. I promise that from today onwards I would perform my duties more sincerely than before." Saying this Yamraj went to his abode. Thereafter, all the people and the king Abhinand got up and prayed in praise of Lord Ganesha.

The fire of the *yajna* was lit up again. The religious ceremony was completed without any obstacles. This is how Ganesha protected the *yajna* of king Abhinand.

GANESHA IN THE FORM OF EKDANTA

This is a saga of olden times. The son of sage Chyavan called Madasur was very brave. He wanted to rule over the whole universe. Therefore, he went to Shukracharya, the *guru* of demons. After introducing himself to the *guru* he expressed his desire and said, "I am the son of sage Chyavan. I wish to rule over the whole universe and spread the demon's influence all over. But I cannot do anything without your help. I need your guidance. Kindly make me your pupil."

Guru Shukracharya was very impressed by Madasur and said, "Listen, Madasur, from now onwards you are my disciple. Go and worship Goddess Bhagvati and get a boon." Saying this he gave *Ekakshri* (one holy word) *mantra* to him and blessed him.

Madasur bowed to him and then went to the forest to worship the Goddess. He meditated for years and at last, the Goddess appeared and said, "I am pleased with you. Ask for anything

you want." Madasur begged with folded hands, "Please bless me with the power by virtue of which I can conquer the whole universe. Also bestow me with good health throughout my life."

Goddess Bhagvati granted the boon and disappeared. Thereafter, Madasur organised a big army of demons and declared himself as their king. At first he conquered the earth and then captured the heaven. He also sent his army to the nether world and conquered it as well. In this way he became the king the whole of universe.

Now all the universe had come under the demons' control. The atrocities of the demons began to increase. They banned the worship of Gods and other religious activities. Gods and sages hid themselves in the caves.

All the Gods went to sage Sanatkumar for help. He advised them to worship Lord Ekdanta who could help them.

The words of sage Sanatkumar gave a new hope to the Gods. They worshipped Lord Ekdanta (another name for Ganesha) for one hundred years. Pleased with their devotion, Lord Ekdanta appeared before the Gods and said, "I am pleased with you. Ask for anything you want."

All the Gods bowed before him and begged with folded hands, "Oh lord! We have been terrified by Madasur. His atrocities have troubled us. The rule of demons forced us to hide in the caves. Please save our lives!" Lord Ekdanta said, "You need not worry now. Soon I would teach a lesson to Madasur." Saying this he disappeared. One day sage Narada went to Madasur and said, "Oh, the king of demons! Your reign seems to be on the verge of its end, as Lord Ekdanta has promised to help the Gods." Sage Narada's words made Madasur worried. He organized a big army and proceeded to attack Lord Ekdanta. Lord Ekdanta was aware of Madasur's intentions. He appeared before him. All the demons were frightened to see him. He was sitting on a big mouse with dreadful weapons in his hands. He said

to Madasur, "Madasur, I warn you that if you do not return the kingdom of the Gods, I'll have to kill you."

Madasur replied, "I have conquered the heaven to rule it. I am not afraid of your threats". Saying this he tried to throw an arrow towards Lord Ekdanta. But even before he could do so, Lord Ekdanta threw a hatchet towards him. The demon became unconscious. After some time when he recovered, he fell on the feet of Ganesha and begged for forgiveness saying, "Oh Lord! forgive me. I could not understand your greatness. I am a big fool."

Lord Ekdanta was kind enough to pardon him. He said, "The only place where you can live now is the nether world. Go there and never visit the place where I am being worshipped." The demon obeyed him and went to the nether world. Seeing their leader going, his army fled. Gods regained the lost heaven. All cheered for Lord Ekdanta and said, *"Om Ganeshaya Namah"*.

THE PUNISHMENT TO DEMON ILWAL

Once upon a time there lived a demon named Ilwal

in the city of Vatapinagar. He was very powerful. He got pleasure in teasing people. He used to annoy people. Harassed by the demon, people approached the great sage Agastya and said, "Oh great sage! the atrocities of the demon Ilwal are increasing day by day. He kills people at his will. Kindly protect us from this demon."

The sage said, "Do not worry now. Go home. The demon will not harass you any more."

Getting such an assurance, the people returned to their homes. But when they saw that their houses were being destroyed by the demon, they rushed back to the sage and said, "Kindly do something! The demon is destroying our houses." Hearing them, sage Agastya went there immediately and warned the demon Ilwal.

He said, "Release the people in your custody and go

from here!"

But the demon did not listen to him and said, "Why are you interfering in my matter. Go and sit in meditation."

The sage got furious. He tied the demon in a net using his *yogic* powers. He said, "Ilwal! Go from here, otherwise I would kill you." Ilwal fell on the feet of the sage and said, "Oh great sage! Forgive me. I would leave this place and never come back again." Hearing the demon, the sage let him go. Ilwal went to the Vindhyachal mountains and lived there for several years. Later on, when he came to know that sage Agastya had left Vatapi, and the city had become very prosperous, he jumped with happiness. He decided to go back to Vatapi posing to be a benevolent person.

On the other hand, in the absence of the sage, the people of Vatapi had become corrupt and irreligious. The people were morally degraded and took no interest in the religion or worship of Gods. Ilwal decided to take advantage of this situation.

Within no time, Ilwal was able to win the confidence of the people.

There was a statue of Lord Ganesha in Vatapi. Ilwal decided to remove the statue so that any possibility of the people to change back to religious activities should also end. He was of the opinion that the statue might remind the people of the moral values the sage had taught. So, he wanted to remove it at all cost.

Ilwal was very keen to change the attitude of the people and spread irreligious thoughts. In a nutshell, he wanted to reestablish his influence in the city of Vatapi.

Ilwal destroyed the sermons of sage Agastya, that were written on the rocks and stones. Several irreligious people helped him in this work.

The demon's plan worked. People began fighting with each other. There was terror and

chaos everywhere. After destroying all signs of sage Agastya, Ilwal wanted to break the statue of Lord Ganesha. Knowing about the presence of Ilwal in the city, other demons also joined him. They discussed how to remove the statue of Ganesha, which was still giving inspiration to people to adopt the ethical values. Hence, one day all the devils went to break the statue of Ganesha. But as they raised their big hammer, there was a big explosion which resulted in the death of all the demons.

Ilwal was alive but he had lost one leg and a hand. He was now handicapped and was repenting for his misdeeds. Soon he heard a voice that was coming from the statue, "Ilwal! You'll have to spend the rest of your life as a handicapped person. This is the punishment for all your sins." Thereafter, the religious and ethical values were reestablished in the city of Vatapi.

HP